Canyon Country

by WAYNE RANNEY

Sedona area. Photograph by Tom Johnson

Opposite: *Winter storm over Grand Canyon.*
Photograph by Tom Danielsen

Introduction

No place in the world is quite like the American Southwest, and perhaps no other region has areas known by so many different names. One of these areas, the Colorado Plateau to most of us, is the Four Corners region to economists and politicians. Many promoters refer to it as Color Country, and at least one map maker has labeled it Indian Country. But most descriptively, it is Canyon Country, which can be found in the redrock deserts and forested highlands of Arizona, Utah, Colorado, and New Mexico.

The Colorado Plateau is the Four Corners region to economists and politicians. Promoters refer to it as Color Country, and at least one map maker has labeled it Indian Country. No matter what it is called, its geological diversity is unparalled.

Within the region's variably defined boundaries, a multitude of canyons, arroyos, washes, draws, gullies, and gulches snake across the land like lightning in the summer sky. Canyons *made* this country. Most of the other landforms—buttes, cliffs, mesas—are byproducts created and destroyed during the life cycle of canyons. Like living entities, canyons experience birth and growth. Sometimes, they lose a limb as they mature, and eventually they die.

A Southwestern Lani

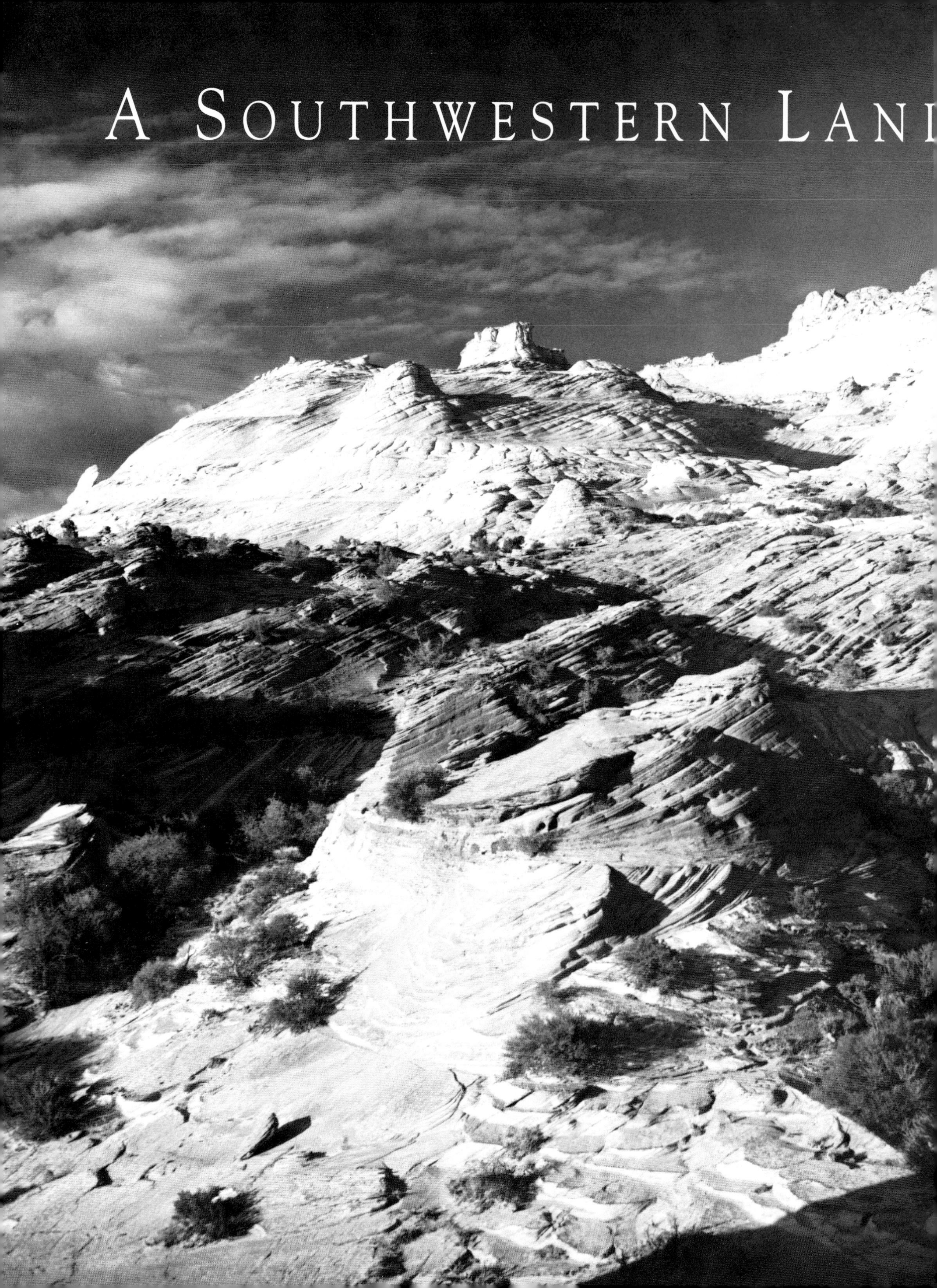

SCAPE

avajo Sandstone. Photograph by Don Keller

What is a Canyon ?

The word "canyon" comes from the Spanish cañon (pronounced can-yown) and was brought to the area by the conquistadores. Cana (derived from the Latin canna for cane) means long tube or hollow. The suffix "-on" stands for large, and so cañon literally means a large hole or opening. Anglicized, the word canyon is now as common as mountain or river.

Many first-time observers of the Grand Canyon believe canyons are created by a giant crack in the earth and that rivers later occupied these canyons. But a closer look clarifies the real relationship between canyons and rivers.

Here is how an ordinary canyon begins. First, imagine that a piece of earth is raised above sea level. Any rain that falls on this virgin landscape will run downhill, creating a drainage. Initially, the stream will have a very low gradient, or slope, and may meander wildly across the featureless terrain. If the forces that first raised the land continue, however, the drainage may straighten its course (if the uplift is rapid) or become confined in its meanderings (if the uplift is gradual).

Through time—and time is the key here—a river may become entrenched within the rising walls of the landscape. If it does, a canyon is born.

Once the river has cut through the land, other forces of erosion widen a canyon's walls. Many visitors to the Grand Canyon think that the Colorado River was 10 miles wide at one time because that is the width (rim to rim) of today's canyon. In reality, however, the river has always been about as wide as it is now. The canyon's rim is wider than the bottom because the river cut the rim first, thus exposing it to wind, rain, freezing, and thawing for a much longer period.

A canyon's shape is determined by the type of rock that composes it. If a drainage system cuts through a stack of hard rocks, such as granite, sandstone, or schist, a U-shaped or slot canyon will result. These canyons do not widen appreciably because the rock is resistant to other forces of erosion. Only the river can shape it. A canyon cut into softer rocks, like shale, siltstone, or clay, will assume a V-shape profile because wind and rain widen the soft rock as readily as the river deepens it.

Most larger canyons have a characteristic stairstep profile of cliff-slope-cliff, which reflects the alternating layers of hard (cliff) and soft (slope) rock types. Deep canyons such as Grand Canyon, Cataract Canyon, and those along the San Juan River display this profile.

What is Canyon Country?

What defines the Canyon Country and where exactly is it located? First, we must look at the Colorado Plateau, which, with a few notable exceptions, is synonymous with Canyon Country. The plateau is a region defined by the presence of relatively flat-lying sedimentary rocks and surrounded on all sides by rocks that have been more intensely faulted, folded, and deformed. On its western side, the Colorado Plateau is marked by the Wasatch Front, high cliffs formed by faults that run from Salt Lake City to St. George, Utah. South of St. George, the Grand Wash Cliffs at the western end of the Grand Canyon form a clearly defined, impressive edge to the plateau. These cliffs wrap around to the southwest and essentially merge with the Mogollon Rim, considered to be the southern boundary of the Colorado Plateau.

Geologists have had some difficulty determining a precise position for the plateau's southeastern boundary. Because streams have cut spectacular canyons into the Mogollon Rim, we will look at a few canyons occurring beyond the generally accepted southern limit of the plateau. The Salt and Verde rivers, which flow through these canyons, receive most of their runoff from the plateau's southern edge and will serve well as a boundary for our definition of Canyon Country.

The eastern edge of the Colorado Plateau is also blurred. The Rio Grande clearly separates the plateau from the Great Plains to the east, but north of its headwaters the boundary between the Colorado Plateau and Rocky Mountains must be drawn with a

dotted line. The problem arises because of the complex setting and origin of the San Juan Mountains in southwestern Colorado. This volcanic range was extruded onto a plateau similar to today's Colorado Plateau sometime between 25 and 35 million years ago. After the volcanic eruptions, rivers cut into the growing mountains and carved a wonderful series of canyons. Black Canyon of the Gunnison is only one of the many that we will include in our definition of Canyon Country. Thus, the Continental Divide north of the Rio Grande will be used here as the eastern edge of Canyon Country.

The northern boundary for both the Colorado Plateau and Canyon Country is the Uinta Mountains in northeast Utah.

Canyons are a relatively common geological feature throughout the world, and a few are even more spectacular than some found in Canyon Country. But nowhere on Earth is there the great concentration or system of canyons as that found in the southwestern United States. But why here, why not Montana or Minnesota?

To understand why Canyon Country is unique, we must know something about the processes that have acted in concert throughout a long span of time. Five factors make the southwestern canyons unique: (1) the type of rock found in the area, (2) the color of the rocks, (3) the relative lack of deformation or disturbance, (4) an arid climate, and (5) the presence of large rivers.

Above: *Chinle Formation. Photograph by Tom Danielsen*

Opposite, left: *Colorful rock strata typify Canyon Country. Photograph by Tom Danielsen*

Opposite, right: *River boulders. Photograph by Ralph Lee Hopkins*

What makes Canyon Country unique?

Rock Type

The bedrock geology of the region, especially the history of sedimentation, is the first factor that makes this land what it is today. This is a land made up primarily of sedimentary rocks. For a mind-boggling span of 500 million years, from 570 to 70 million years ago, Canyon Country was a relatively flat, low-lying area near the coast of ancient North America. In these near-shore environments, sediments many thousands of feet thick accumulated and were buried throughout the years. This happened because the earth's crust both warped up and buckled down in response to the drifting of the continents over the surface of the planet. When drifting continents collide with one another, mountains are formed. When continents break apart, the land subsides, and sediments are deposited. Most geologists believe that about 570 million years ago, North America split apart from the continents of Australia and Antarctica and that it has not collided with any large landmass since. This splitting apart created a quiet, or passive, margin at what is now Arizona and Utah.

Continental drift was set in motion by the variations of heat flow from the interior of the earth: uprising plumes of heat caused the crust to become buoyant and arch up, while cooler areas became dense and warped downward. Not only was the Canyon Country situated on a passive margin, it also must have been located over a relatively cool area because the great stack of sedimentary rock suggests ongoing subsidence.

A similar environment is present today within the Gulf of Mexico, where approximately 65,000 feet of sediment has been accumulating in a subsiding basin for the last 150 million years. The gulf was created when South America broke apart from North America in the split up of the last great supercontinent, Pangaea. Some geologists have speculated that a future Canyon Country could be created when these gulf sediments are eroded. Even if they are correct, we won't be around to see it.

Color

Minerals within the sedimentary rocks of the Canyon Country play a significant role in creating this unique landscape. Specifically, various forms of iron have created the kaleidoscope of color in the canyonlands. All the reds, purples, magentas, oranges, browns, mauves, and even greens in the rocks result from the oxidation or reduction (essentially, rust and antirust) of iron in particular chemical environments.

Where did the iron come from? Again, we must look to the condi-

The brilliantly colored rocks in Canyon Country have been created by varying amounts and kinds of iron. Just 0.5 percent is enough to tint a clear sand grain.

tions present when the sedimentary layers were laid down. From 320 to 120 million years ago, the area was generally elevated above sea level, and rocks of terrestrial origin (as opposed to marine) were preserved. River floodplains, sandy deserts, or seasonal lakes were some of the many environments that came and went over this 200-million-year span. The source of the sediment and iron was the mountains that bordered the future Canyon Country. These mountains often consisted of granite or other crystalline rocks rich in iron-bearing mica. When these mountains were eroded, the granites were broken up and their components eventually became other rock. Durable quartz crystals were rolled in rivers or blown by wind into sand-

stone layers. Crystals of feldspar released their clay constituents and became layers of mudstone and shale. Mica crystals released their oxidized iron.

The iron, migrating in groundwater, permeated the newly deposited sediments, coating their grains with a thin veil of color. Some of the most brilliant red rocks in Canyon Country contain only 0.5 percent iron by volume, and just a thin coating is enough to tint a clear sand grain. Different concentrations of iron result in completely different rock colors. Varying amounts of the mineral hematite create the brilliant reds, oranges, and purples. Yellows and golds are from limonite, another oxide of iron. Reduced iron (or iron that has not been in contact with oxygen) produces green. This color tends to concentrate in fine-grained sediment where oxygen has been excluded.

Lack of disturbance

If a good number of areas on Earth do evolve with the first two conditions met (great stacks of sedimentary rocks derived mostly in continental settings), the third factor narrows the field considerably: preservation of the thick, colorful strata in a relatively unfolded and unfaulted state. This characteristic distinguishes Canyon Country from the adjoining physiographic provinces such as the Basin and Range in Arizona and Nevada and the Rocky Mountains in Colorado and Wyoming. Faults and folds do occur on the Colorado Plateau; in fact, some of the region's most spectacular features are its great monoclines, where compression of the earth's crust has caused the sedimentary layers to bow upward. But as a whole, Canyon Country is flat-lying, or at most gently tilted.

This relative lack of deformation is the result of equal, even uplift over a broad region. The reasons for this type of uplift are unknown. Rising plumes of heat, generated by radioactive decay within the earth, may have caused the area to rise buoyantly en masse. The great thickness of the sedimentary pile may have acted like a giant insulating blanket as heat accumulated under the plateau. This area, which was relatively cool and subsiding for a long time, may have finally collected enough heat under it about 70 million years ago to begin uplifting. During this period, we also know that North America, in its westward drift away from Africa and Europe, began to override a piece of oceanic crust to the west, causing the Rocky Mountains to form. The Colorado Plateau probably rose in elevation as a result of these pressures — much like a hot air balloon rises through the cool morning air.

The uplift is perhaps continuing, and about 2,000 feet of uplift may have occurred over the last five million years. But why the Canyon Country was spared the intense faulting and folding that ripped through

Barrel cactus in Middle Granite Gorge, Grand Canyon. Photograph by Ralph Lee Hopkins

Nevada and the Rocky Mountains remains a mystery. We must satisfy ourselves for now with the understanding that this type of uplift has allowed the sedimentary rocks of Canyon Country to remain preserved essentially as they were when they formed.

Top: Dry conditions preserve much of the southwestern landscape. Photograph by Tom Danielsen

Bottom: Rock formations of the Bisti Wilderness illustrate the erosional force of wind. Photograph by Dale Schicketanz

Opposite: Goosenecks of the San Juan River. Photograph by Tom Brownold

Arid Climate

The present climate of the plateau is arid. Without these dry conditions, the landscape would be shrouded in clouds or covered under a dense veil of vegetation. Exciting new studies have suggested that the uplift of continental plateaus such as the Tibetan Plateau in Asia and the Colorado Plateau in the American Southwest may have played a major role in determining atmospheric circulation patterns of Earth—and thus its climate. These studies even postulate that the uplift of these plateaus may have been the driving force that created the ice ages about three million years ago.

Briefly, the creation of these two great plateaus changed the seasonal distribution of temperature and rainfall. Before this time, atmospheric circulation was relatively simple; plant fossils show that much of the planet had a warm, equable climate throughout the year. When the plateaus were uplifted, they deflected air-flow patterns so that a summer monsoon season was created on and near them, with a cooler, drier regime affecting areas to the west. Witness the summer rains in India and Arizona and the foggy but dry summers of California and the Mediterranean, both located west of the major plateau influencing their weather. The ramifications of this change were monumental. Magnolia trees disappeared from summer-dry California. Drought-tolerant prairie grasses replaced trees on the Great Plains, encouraging the spread of animals like the bison. And cold, dry tundra environments were created "downwind" from the uplifted areas in the Arctic and Siberia. In these cooled environments, the growth of ice sheets was enhanced.

The uplift of these plateaus also may have helped to remove carbon dioxide (CO_2) from the atmosphere. This happens because uplifted plateaus expose silica-rich continental crust, which reacts with the carbon dioxide in rainwater to form carbonic acid. This, in turn, is delivered by rivers to the sea, where plankton and coral use it to build their shells. In this way, CO_2 is taken from the atmosphere and stored on the sea floor for millions of years. It eventually will be recycled back into the atmosphere via volcanic processes, but in the short term, less carbon dioxide in the atmosphere means cooler air temperatures.

Local features also have contributed to the general aridity of the Canyon Country. The region is located in the rain shadow of the Sierra Nevada and Transverse Mountains of California. Winter moisture from the

Gulf of Alaska, which otherwise might drench the Colorado Plateau, is instead dumped on the mountains to the west. Additionally, Canyon Country is located at a latitude conducive to the formation of deserts— about 30 degrees North. If this part of North America were 15 degrees farther south or north, the great red rocks could be covered in a tropical or temperate rain forest.

Aridity is often considered the most important factor in making Canyon Country unique. But it is aridity of a distinctive type—one that includes large storms dumping lots of moisture in short (but widely spaced) periods of time. It is this "flashy" climate that results in the formation of deep, narrow canyons.

Great Rivers

A fifth and final condition, the presence of great rivers, distinguishes Canyon Country. These agents of change have carved and sculpted the land. Although it may seem paradox-ical to have both an arid climate and large rivers, there are examples. The Nile River in Egypt and the Tigris and Euphrates rivers in Iraq are large rivers in arid environments, but they occupy wide, broad valleys close to sea level. Missing today, though they may have existed in the past, are the great canyons.

In Canyon country, the Colorado River is the master stream, the very heart of this region's great system of canyons. In its 1,450-mile journey to the sea, the Colorado has carved spectacular chasms—Glenwood Canyon in the Rocky Mountains, Ruby and Westwater canyons, Canyonlands, Glen Canyon, and the incomparable Grand Canyon. In addition, the secondary rivers of the system, the Green, Gunnison, Dolores, Yampa, and San Juan, have also cut stupendous canyons on their way to the master stream.

The Green River has carved Horseshoe and Red canyons in Wyoming and Lodore, Echo, Whirlpool, and Desolation canyons downstream in northeast Utah. These are some of the most rugged and seldom-visited landscapes in all of Canyon Country. The Gunnison River has cut the marvelous Black Canyon of the Gunnison, reminis-cent of the depths of Grand Canyon but lacking the upper redrock "icing." Although not officially on the Colorado Plateau, Black Canyon is an important part of Canyon Country. The Dolores River canyons in westernmost Colorado probably are the least known of any of the region's great chasms. Unfortunately, the Dolores was dammed recently, and although the canyons remain, the river is merely a vestige of its for-mer greatness. The Yampa River in northwestern Colorado, which many people consider one of the most beautiful, is now the only major drainage in the system without an impoundment. The San Juan River remains one of the Southwest's best-known and most-visited rivers.

Yet Canyon Country is much more than these grand vistas or stu-pendous landscapes. There are hid-den places where a person can find more intimate beauty, more enclosed solitude. Often nameless, these places offer the amplified sound of water trickling in a cool sandstone amphitheater or the smell of a pine tree as the wind whisks through a bend in the narrows. Here, in these secret places, Canyon Country reach-es unparalleled beauty. Others that are named—Slickhorn Gulch, Whirlwind Draw, Tsegi Canyon, Death Hollow, Arroyo Hondo, and Antelope Canyon—evoke images of a world still unfound and mystical.

In an area so blessed with spectac-ular canyons, it is difficult to choose just a few for description here. The canyons that follow were selected to represent a variety of areas and canyon-forming processes.

THE CANYONS *of*
CANYON COUNTRY

Salt River Canyon

Mention the words Salt River to many Arizonans and visions of dry sand, gravel pits, and auto dumps come to mind. Modern man has not been kind to the lower sections of this desert river. But many miles upstream from the sprawl of metropolitan Phoenix, the Salt River is as wild and free as it was when the Apache gathered mesquite beans and cactus fruit along its banks. This portion of the river has carved a series of canyons that form the southern boundary of Canyon Country. One of these canyons, seen where U.S. Highway 60 crosses the river north of Globe, is known as "Little Grand Canyon." Although not as deep as its more famous counterpart, the Salt River Canyon shares a similar geological history. Exposed in the walls of the Salt River Canyon is rock that is about one billion years old, a time when cyanobacteria (blue-green algae) was the most advanced form of life.

The Salt River Canyon began forming about 70 million years ago, when what is now central Arizona was lifted higher than the future Canyon Country to the north. Ancient rivers cut a canyon at least 18 miles long, about 2,500 feet deep, and a few miles wide. Gravels derived from the ancient highlands and the walls of the old canyon can still be found northeast of the Highway 60 bridge. These gravels, now perched high on the Mogollon Rim, could only have come from the southwest. This means the river that cut the first canyon flowed in the exact opposite direction of today's Salt River! Later events in the area help to explain this amazing drainage reversal.

The cliffs of Salt River Canyon. Photograph by Dale Schicketanz

Twenty to 25 million years ago, explosive and devastating volcanic eruptions buried the ancient canyon with thick, hot sheets of ash. We call the remnants of these sheets the Apache Leap Tuff, named after the high cliff near Globe, Arizona, where certain Apache warriors jumped to their death rather than surrender to a life on the reservation. At the time of the volcanic eruptions, the ancient highlands were destroyed when they were faulted lower than the uplifted Colorado Plateau. This rearrangement of the land caused the runoff in the area to reverse, flowing from the Mogollon Rim to the southwest and leading to the formation of the modern Salt River.

But how and why did the Salt River cut its canyon exactly where the ancient river had flowed? Was it a coincidence? Or can we play detective once more and look to the rocks for an answer? The answer to the question can be found in the deposits of volcanic ash. The thick accumulations of ash within the ancient canyon contracted when they cooled. This contraction would have been the greatest where the ash was thickest: on top of the ancient river, the deepest part of the canyon. A broad, gentle valley probably developed directly above the course of the old river; when new drainages were created, they would have flowed in this broad valley. Thus, the change in flow direction resulted from a new river cutting through land on top of an older river that went in the other direction.

In addition to the main Salt River Canyon, many tributary streams feeding the river have carved significant canyons in their own right. In fact, the river derives 95 percent of its runoff from northern tributaries—including Carrizo, Corduroy, Cibeque, Canyon, and Cherry creeks. ♦

Fossil Canyon

Left: *Fossil Creek*

Above: *Fossil Creek is a popular oasis for south-western wildlife. Photographs by Tom Brownold*

Fossil Canyon was named for the impressions of cottonwood, willow, and sycamore leaves encased in the limestone deposits around Fossil Springs. The water from these springs is rich in liquid calcium. When the water emerges from the ground, minerals precipitate out as a solid limestone called travertine. Freshly fallen leaves become trapped in the ever-forming layers of limestone. When the leaf decays, a fossil imprint remains. Fossil Springs lets us witness the birth of cool, sweet water in the desert, an experience rarely equaled in the natural world.

Fossil Canyon is tributary to the Verde River. Like the Salt River Canyon and its tributaries, the canyon originates high atop the Mogollon Rim. The upper part of the canyon is normally bone dry, only running with water during the spring melt or after a classic Canyon Country summer thunderstorm.

Visitation to this part of the canyon is practically nil. Boulder-hopping downstream will eventually bring you within sight and smell of a beautiful grove of green cottonwoods and lush sycamores. Unexpectedly, water begins to trickle from the ground. Soon more water issues from the rocks. For more than a quarter mile, dozens of springs emerge until the stream flows freely in a symphony of running water. It feels much more like the heart of a temperate rain forest than the edge of the Sonoran Desert.

Innumerable birds nest in the forest canopy, and deer, foxes, and mountain lions have sipped water from the springs for millennia.

High above this verdant paradise, black basalt shimmers in the desert sun. This basalt was once hot fluid lava, and like the water at Fossil Springs, it too emerged from the depths of the earth near Fossil Canyon. Fossil Springs probably has its origins in groundwater forced to the surface when it encounters these massive basalts. ◆

Oak Creek Canyon

Between five and eight million years ago, this old canyon was buried in a series of lava flows that erupted from within and on top of the canyon rim.

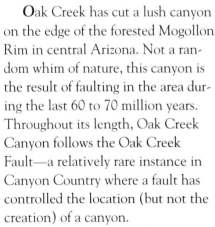

Oak Creek has cut a lush canyon on the edge of the forested Mogollon Rim in central Arizona. Not a random whim of nature, this canyon is the result of faulting in the area during the last 60 to 70 million years. Throughout its length, Oak Creek Canyon follows the Oak Creek Fault—a relatively rare instance in Canyon Country where a fault has controlled the location (but not the creation) of a canyon.

The canyon we see today is not the first one cut on top of this fault. A previous canyon existed here before eight million years ago, though its exact shape is unknown because most of it is still covered up. Canyons frequently occur in fault zones because faulted rocks, crushed under the strain of earth movements and water, furnish relatively nonresistant paths for water. This ancestral canyon followed the fault line for a longer distance than the modern canyon. Gravels that once formed the floor of ancestral Oak Creek Canyon can be found near Slide Rock State Park.

Between five and eight million years ago, this old canyon was buried in a series of lava flows that erupted from within and on top of the canyon rim. At least five different lava flows can be seen near Indian Gardens on Highway 89A. Some are separated by thin horizons of gravel, indicating that the stream tried to reestablish itself on top of the flows. After the canyon was filled with basalt, a second period of faulting began. Modern Oak Creek Canyon has, for the most part, cut through this faulted zone. For some reason, however, the new canyon leaves the fault zone near Grasshopper Point, and Oak Creek flows southwest of the fault zone. That is why the canyon has such an asymmetrical profile above Grasshopper Point (with black basalt on the east side and red rocks on the west) and occurs solely in the colorful red rocks below that point.

To understand why a creek would leave the easy-to-erode confines of a fault zone, we need to look up the

When the creek exited the confines of its canyon and spread out in the wide Verde Valley, it deposited an apron of coarse, rocky debris. That deposit is about 1½ miles long, about a half mile wide, and 100 feet thick and has a gradient of about 80 feet per mile—just slightly steeper than the modern creek. This sheet of mostly black basalt cobbles with some redrock pebbles is identical to what is found in the creek today. The deposit is wider to the southwest and points northeast towards the mouth of Oak Creek Canyon. But this deposit lies 700 feet above the modern creek. That means that Oak Creek has cut that deep since the deposit was laid down.

Unfortunately, no fossils have yet been found that would tell the age of the cobble deposit, but by using other evidence from the area, geologists have set a tentative age of 1.5 million years. Thus, Oak Creek may be cutting down into the red rocks at a rate of about one foot every 2,150 years. To see this revealing cobble deposit, go to the top of Table Top Mountain, also known as Airport Mesa. It seems that the aviation pioneers found this old Oak Creek deposit an ideal place for landing airplanes! ♦

drainage when thinking of its origins rather than down. Oak Creek expanded in a headward fashion back through a block of red rocks until it encountered the Oak Creek Fault, where it has continued to expand headward in the more easily eroded fault zone.

Opposite, left: *View from the Mogollon Rim. Photograph by Tom Johnson*

Center: *Lower end of the fault area. Photograph by Dick Dietrich*

Left: *Oak Creek. Photograph by Tom Johnson*

Above, right: *Sedona's brilliant red sandstone cliffs. Photograph by Tom Johnson*

The Black Canyon of the Gunnison.
Photograph by Tom Danielsen

Opposite: Detail of the Black Canyon's
schist and granite. Photograph by
Jeff Behan

Black Canyon of the Gunnison

Thirty million years of erosion stripped away overlying rocks and

exposed the top of the black schist in the floor of a flat valley.

The Black Canyon of the Gunnison is one of the most impressive gorges in all of Canyon Country. Its near-vertical walls of schist and granite rise to 3,000 feet above the Gunnison River in western Colorado. It is a perfect example of how resistant rocks form a very large, but narrow, U-shaped canyon. These hard, ancient rocks, the roots of a long-eroded mountain range, are between 1,400 and 1,700 million years old. The canyon itself, however, is just a fraction of that age.

Black Canyon of the Gunnison is made more interesting because just north and south of it smaller streams have cut broad valleys. At first, this seems illogical, but a look at the events of the last 60 million years, as recorded in the rocks of the area, reveals the answer. At that time, a

blister on the earth's crust, an upwarp, was created where the Black Canyon is today. This blister was produced when the Rocky Mountains were squeezed into existence and the 1,700-million-year-old schists were arched up near the surface of the earth. Thirty million years of erosion stripped away overlying rocks and exposed the top of the black schist in the floor of a flat valley. If events had stopped here, about 30 million years ago, the Black Canyon would never have come into existence because the hard rocks would have deflected growing drainages north or south of the upwarp into softer rock units.

Around 28 million years ago, however, huge volcanic eruptions occurred north and south of the area. To the south, the great San Juan Mountains were formed. The West

Elk Mountains began building to the north. Lava flows and ash eruptions spread violently from their eruptive centers, and the old drainage system was pushed farther away from the growing volcanic ranges. Eventually, a single major drainage was developed in the valley between the overlapping ash sheets of the San Juan and West Elk volcanic centers. The location of this valley, and the ancestral Gunnison River, happened to be on top of the old upwarp of black schist.

Soon, the river became entrenched in the ash flows. When the entire plateau was uplifted, the Gunnison River had no choice but to cut a canyon through the underlying ancient schist. Eventually, the lower slopes of the volcanoes eroded away, leaving the confusing landscape relationships that we see today.

This beautiful canyon is surprisingly young. From a 1.2-million-year-old layer of volcanic ash at what must have been river level, the river has cut down an additional 1,200 feet. This means that the canyon we see today is perhaps two million years old. Today, two-thirds of Black Canyon is buried under the waters of three upstream reservoirs. But within Black Canyon of the Gunnison National Monument, the river still runs through this impressive slash in the earth's crust. ◆

Antelope Canyon

On the Colorado Plateau, one type of canyon often arouses inquiry. This is the hidden but sought-after slot canyon occasionally encountered when exploring the plateau's back-country. A slot canyon is difficult to find because it is so narrow, often only as wide as a pair of outstretched arms. Although these relatively deep canyons twist and turn, they do not change significantly in width from bottom to top. Most often, these canyons can be entered only from upstream or downstream. Slot canyons typically are young features that have formed in only the last few thousand years. Antelope Canyon serves as an example.

Antelope Canyon is located on the Navajo Indian Reservation southeast of Page, Arizona, near the Navajo Generating Station. A walk up this canyon is a fantastic journey into the heart of Canyon Country. The stream has cut a vertical but twisting slot through the Navajo Sandstone. This famous strata was deposited about 190 million years ago during the "Age of Dinosaurs" in a large Saharalike desert. You can see evidence of the large dune fields in the many angular crossbeds in the canyon walls. Since crossbeds form on the lee, or downwind, side of a sand dune, they tell us what the prevailing wind direction was at the time. Most crossbeds in the Navajo Sandstone dip to the south, indicating that 190 million years ago the wind blew out of the north. But how did the narrow slot canyon form?

To answer this question, we must exit Antelope Canyon and look at the surrounding terrain. To the west, Navajo Sandstone is exposed in a cliff, but a large section of the cliff is missing. This missing sandstone is replaced by loose sand that appears to have filled in an old canyon.

The same events created Antelope Canyon. An ancient stream cut a relatively wide canyon into the Navajo Sandstone, but in the not-too-distant past this canyon was filled with loose, wind-blown sand. When the canyon was completely choked with sand, the stream had to find another route to the Colorado River. The climate during this dry time was "flashy," which means it was generally dry, but when it did rain, it usually came all at once in flashfloods. This infrequent but voluminous runoff carved the slot into the soft Navajo Sandstone. ♦

The Navajo Sandstone of Antelope Canyon.
Photograph by Tom Brownold

Opposite, left: *Rappeling into Antelope Canyon.*
Photograph by George Stocking

Opposite, right: *Solid rock in fluid form.*
Photograph by Gary Ladd

Grand Gulch

The words "gulch" and "gully" were derived from the French gullet, which in turn came from the Latin gula, meaning throat. These relatively small, narrow canyons do seem to completely enclose a stream. Cowboys described any canyon where there was no ready way out as a gulch. Another generation of canyoneers has made its way into the myriad of gulches and gullies found within the Canyon Country—finding a few favorites. One of the most marvelous is Grand Gulch, a twisting, tortuous tributary of the San Juan River in southeast Utah.

Grand Gulch is most famous for its well-preserved cliff dwellings built by the Anasazi who lived in the canyon about a thousand years ago. Within the 65-mile serpentine length of Grand Gulch, hundreds of prehistoric sites can be found in alcoves or overhangs cut into the Cedar Mesa Sandstone. The alcoves form as groundwater flows down through the sandstone and is then forced out horizontally by a layer of clay or other impervious rock. A spring flows out at these points, eroding the base of the sandstone. Through time, considerable portions of the undercut roof will fall away, eventually leaving an alcove or overhang. Not only does the process form a perfect place to get out of the rain or the summer sun, it also delivers water right to the front door!

It is curious that Grand Gulch has cut such a sinuous canyon in a layer of rock as resistant as the Cedar Mesa Sandstone—and at precisely this spot on the elevated Grand Gulch Plateau. Normally, such sinuous streams develop their course in softer rocks and are confined within valleys. There are no faults along the length of the gulch, so it did not develop here for that reason. Can we find any evidence that Grand Gulch may have developed in a valley that had soft rocks in its floor?

From the rim of Grand Gulch, the Red House Cliffs are the most prominent landscape feature to the west. This high escarpment was formed by a bulge in the earth's crust (the Monument Upwarp), which caused the rock layers to bend upward into an arch about 30 miles wide. Erosion eventually removed the layers on top, leaving a ring of strata that encircled the bulge. Over time, this ring widened—creating today's landscape. The Red House Cliffs mark the western side of the upwarp, with Monument Valley, Comb Ridge, and Canyonlands forming the south, east, and north sides, respectively.

If we were to reconstruct the ancient landscape, the Red House Cliffs would assume their former position on top of the Grand Gulch Plateau. A valley would be located where Grand Gulch is today—between the ancient Red House Cliffs on the west and the rising surface of the Grand Gulch Plateau to the east.

At this time, the stream in Grand Gulch must have been flowing at the base of the cliffs on top of the Organ Rock or Chinle formations, possibly explaining how the sinuous course of the stream developed. Since Grand Gulch does parallel the Red House Cliffs, this theory is both plausible and persuasive.

Why then didn't Grand Gulch continue to migrate to the west within the retreating shales of the Red House Cliffs? Perhaps those cliffs were stabilized long enough for the stream to become entrenched. If this period of stabilization occurred during the ice age, wetter conditions would have retarded the rate of cliff retreat by providing the landscape with a protective cover of vegetation. (Keep in mind that the Colorado Plateau was being uplifted at this time—and uplift will cause streams to cut deeper into a rising mass of rock.) Whatever its origins, and however complex, Grand Gulch is a wonderful spot to ponder the Southwest's diversity. ♦

Above: *Unnamed ruins, Grand Gulch Primitive Area, Utah. Photograph by Jonathan A. Meyers*

Left: *Grand Gulch. Photograph by Jonathan A. Meyers*

Bryce Canyon

Bryce Canyon National Park might seem an unusual area to include in a story about canyons. After all, the national park is not really a true canyon at all; rather, it is a cliff or escarpment. One small canyon within the park, named Bryce Canyon after pioneer Ebenezer Bryce, has given this much-visited geological wonderland its name. Mormon settlers, however, called the cliffs the "Bryce Breaks" because of the significant break in topography that the escarpment makes. Bryce belongs in our look at canyons because here, more than perhaps anywhere else in all of Canyon Country, we find evidence for how the area's rivers may have evolved and grown in the last five or six million years.

River systems evolve and grow through a process known as "stream piracy." This process probably played a major role in the development of the Grand Canyon and the evolution of the Colorado River system. Stream piracy occurs when rivers differ dramatically in their gradient (some drop rapidly while others flow more gently). Steep drainages cut into their headlands at a much more vigorous rate than those with low gradients because water flowing down a steep gradient can carry more sediment. Eventually, these fast-eroding

Opposite, above: *Main amphitheater, Bryce Canyon. Photograph by Tom Danielsen*

Opposite, below: *Thor's Hammer. Photograph by Tom Danielsen*

Left: *Fairyland. Photograph by Dale Schicketanz*

streams retreat into the bed of another river, capturing its waters.

At Bryce, we can see these forces at work. A map of the area shows that the cliffs are only the western edge of a huge erosional "amphitheater." The Paria River has cut this semicircular feature into the vibrantly colored strata of the Claron (or Wasatch) Formation. Nearby stands Table Mountain, the eastern edge of the Paria Amphitheater. The gradients of the many tributaries of the Paria River in Bryce are steep, dropping about 700 feet per mile. Just west of the park is the East Fork of the Sevier River, an older drainage system with a gradient of only 70 feet per mile.

Because the gradients differ so radically, the "Bryce Breaks" will erode or retreat to the west at a much faster rate that any of the tributaries of the Sevier River will erode to the east. Before too long, a section of the Bryce Breaks will retreat west and erode through the

bed of the East Fork. Then, all the runoff that used to go down the East Fork of the Sevier will go into the Paria River.

This branch of the Sevier River will have been "beheaded," or captured, by the Paria. Water that flowed into Sevier Lake in the Great Basin will be diverted instead into the Colorado River system—and, ultimately, the Pacific Ocean. Incidentally, the rate of retreat for the escarpment at Bryce has been calculated at about one foot every 65 years—an incredibly fast rate geologically. That means the Paria River will capture or behead the East Fork of the Sevier in about 686,000 years.

This story is repeated frequently in the history of southwestern rivers—and the Colorado River has been the prime beneficiary. As recently as 18 million years ago, most drainages in the southern portions of the Canyon Country drained to the north, opposite that of the modern Colorado River. The many

branches of the Sevier River may be remnants of these ancient, north-flowing systems.

We also know that Baja California broke away from mainland Mexico about 5.5 million years ago, creating the Gulf of California. Drainages that entered the gulf in the region around the lower Colorado may have had their gradients sharply steepened by the synchronous uplift of the plateau. Presumably, these oversteepened streams would have expanded their drainage area farther north and east into the uplifting Colorado Plateau—at the expense of the low-gradient, but well-established, north-flowing systems.

These older drainages were "captured" by the lower Colorado. Soon, the middle and upper Colorado River established itself across the plateau. Older systems were beheaded and incorporated into the youthful, vigorous Colorado River system. Today's rivers reflect these major changes in river patterns. ◆

Canyon de Chelly and Tsegi Canyon

The names Chelly and Tsegi are Spanish and English pronunciations of the Navajo word for canyon, Tseyi', meaning literally, "among the rocks." It is a coincidence, perhaps, that both Canyon de Chelly and Tsegi Canyon share essentially the same name; for while there are similarities between them, there are also some significant differences. Both were preferred living sites for the Anasazi, who built homes close to the canyon floors so they would have good access to their corn and bean fields. Both are cut into red sandstones, though of different ages and rock formations. Both are well watered, or at least were before 100 years ago.

The most notable difference between the two is the appearance of their floors. In Canyon de Chelly, jeeps and other vehicles routinely traverse the wide, flat canyon floor. Tsegi Canyon, with its deep arroyo, presents a much different profile.

The name of the stream that drains Tsegi Canyon, Laguna Creek, gives us a glimpse of what the floor of this canyon may have looked like when the Spaniards first explored it. Laguna means "shallow lake," and early reports verify that this stream was a marshy, sluggish creek that drained from pond to pond. Today, Laguna Creek is entrenched not only within its redrock canyon but also within an arroyo cut 50 to 75 feet deep into the canyon's former bed. Arroyo comes from the Latin arrugia, meaning mine shaft. It generally refers to any stream-cut feature that has steep, if not vertical, sides and a flat bottom. Most canyons in the Southwest contain arroyos. Canyon de Chelly is an exception.

What causes the cutting of arroyos in Canyon Country? Previously, the introduction of cattle and sheep in the 1880s was thought to have influenced arroyo cutting, for this is when the most recent cycle began in the Southwest. Even today, grazing by hoofed animals does little to promote soil stability. The unconsolidated dirt within the walls of arroyos, however, shows at least three previous cycles of cutting and infilling. Since these events predated the introduction of domesticated animals, something else must have been responsible for the cutting of arroyos. On the buried surfaces of these deposits is evidence of human presence. A circular rock hearth complete with charcoal and ash shows

and the resulting changes in vegetative cover) may influence the initiation of arroyo cutting and filling.

But why is there no arroyo in the bottom of Canyon de Chelly? It seems likely that human activities or natural climatic cycles would affect this canyon just as they have for Tsegi Canyon. The answer is not yet known. Perhaps localized uplifts are responsible for the arroyo cutting that occurs in most of Canyon Country, while localized downwarping in the Defiance Plateau and Canyon de Chelly area has precluded arroyo cutting in the recent past. ◆

Opposite: *Sandstone detail. Photograph by Jerry Jacka*

Above: *Canyon de Chelly. Photograph by Dick Dietrich*

Left: *Canyon bottom, Canyon de Chelly. Photograph by Gene Balzer*

that people were here when the arroyos were either cutting or aggrading. The three periods of cut and fill are confined to the last 10,000 years. Humans were present in the Southwest during this time. Is it possible that these arroyo cycles were caused by overuse of the land by prehistoric people? Or, could climatic changes explain arroyo cutting? A favorite current model holds that climatic cycles (changes in rainfall patterns

Grand Canyon

In the short time that humans have interacted with this land-scape, we have behaved as though we could control the rivers and canyons for our benefit. Ultimately, however, nature's equilibrium will be restored.

The Grand Canyon, grandest of all the canyons in Canyon Country, is on everyone's list of "must sees." Among the canyon's amazing statistics is its length—277 miles. If you traveled a highway that followed the Colorado River and drove 70 miles per hour, it would take four hours to get through the Grand Canyon. While a few others are deeper, no other canyon approaches the length of the Grand Canyon. Standing on the South Rim at Hopi Point, you see only one-fifth of the length of Grand Canyon.

Every vista at the canyon tells a story. At a lonely place called Toroweap, on the north side of the canyon, huge volumes of hardened lava are frozen high on the inner walls of Grand Canyon. These rocky bastions are testimony to the fantastic volcanism that occurred here beginning about 1.5 million years ago. But more than that, these rocks provide clues about the evolution of Grand Canyon and the Colorado River.

The statistics are astounding. More than 150 lava flows and 12 major lava dams once constricted the Colorado River. The longest of these dams was 84 miles, and the highest stood 2,330 feet above the river. This highest dam created a reservoir that backed up the river for almost 400 miles. It took 23 years to fill with water and more than 3,000 years to fill with sediment. Once the reservoir filled, the river poured over the top of the lava dam, creating what must have been one of the world's most amazing waterfalls—2,300 feet high

Above, right: *Mt. Sinyala and Esplanade.*
Photograph by Tom Brownold

Above, left: *Elves Chasm. Photograph by*
Tom Brownold

Opposite: *Grand Canyon's South Rim.*
Photograph by Tom Danielsen

and still contained within Grand Canyon!

The destruction of these durable dams occurred rapidly. A dam 20 miles long may have been completely wiped out in only 20,000 years. The cumulative height of all 12 major lava dams, about 11,300 feet, is more than twice the depth of Grand Canyon, yet this amount of lava was probably removed in only 240,000 years. This means the river conceivably could have cut Grand Canyon in as little as 100,000 years. Surprisingly, once a dam was removed, no matter how high or wide its crest, erosion continued only until the predam profile of the river and the canyon walls was attained. This tells us that the Colorado River and the profile of the Grand Canyon is in equilibrium, a kind of comfort zone that cannot be disturbed by some-

thing as trivial as a 2,300-foot wall of basalt. It may also indicate that the primary process in the formation of Canyon Country is neither a long span of geological time nor the day-after-day erosive power of a river. Perhaps the most important component of the Canyon Country landscape is the uplift history of the Colorado Plateau. Uplift could upset this equilibrium, causing the rivers to erode deeper and the walls to expand outward.

Hidden deep within these numbers is another message as well. In the short time that humans have interacted with this landscape, we have behaved as though we could control the rivers and canyons for our benefit. While we may benefit in the short term from this tampering with nature, ultimately, nature's equilibrium will be restored. ◆

CANYON COUNTRY

The more we study our planet through the "microscope"

called Canyon Country, the more we see

that all of its history is connected.

One landscape gives rise to the next—even though those

two are seemingly unrelated. One landscape, now destroyed,

continues to influence another millions of years

after it ceased to exist.

Opposite, top: *Sedona landscape.*
Photograph by Dick Canby

Opposite, bottom: *Glen Canyon area before*
inundation. Photograph by Gary Ladd

Top, left: *Green River overlook.*
Photograph by Tom Danielsen

Top right: *Canyon vista.*
Photograph by George Stocking

Left: *Glen Canyon Dam.*
Photograph by Jerry Jacka

About the Author

Wayne Ranney is a geologist and educator who lives in Flagstaff. A geology instructor at Yavapai College in Prescott, he also works with the Education Department at the Museum of Northern Arizona. His travels include visits to all seven of Earth's continents. This is the second *Plateau* he has written, and he is the author of *Through Time in Sedona*, a book about the redrock country.

Note: *Permission to explore Antelope Canyon must be obtained from the Navajo Nation. Information and directions can be obtained at the visitor center at Glen Canyon Dam near Page.*

Suggested Reading

Baars, D.
  1972 *The Colorado Plateau, A Geologic History*. University of New Mexico Press.
Barnes, F.
  1986 *Utah Canyon Country*. Utah Geographic Series.
Fisher, R.
  1991 *Mystical Canyons of Water, Light, and Stone*. Sunracer Publications.
Lohman, S.
  1974 *The Geologic Story of Canyonlands National Park*. U.S. Geological Survey Bulletin 1327.
Ranney, W.
  1993 *Through Time in Sedona*. Red Lake Books.
Stephens, H. and E. Shoemaker
  1987 *In the Footsteps of John Wesley Powell*. Johnson Publishing Co.

Managing Editor: *Diana C. Lubick*
Editorial Assistant: *Donna A. Boyd*
Graphic Design: *Julie Sullivan*
Printing: *Land O'Sun Printers*
Electronic Imaging: *Northland Printing*
Color Separations: *American Color*

Photographic Credits:
Above, left: *Hikers in Paria Canyon, by Gary Ladd*

Cover, background: *Canyonlands National Park, Utah, by Tom Brownold*

Cover, inset: *Tents and riverboats, Fort Bottom, Canyonlands National Park, Utah, by Jim Maire*

Table of Contents: *Canyon de Chelly, by Dale Schicketanz*